Stories and Extracts from Shakespeare

Selected by David Orme

Contents

Longman

Edinburgh Gate
Harlow, Essex

The Tempest

The Story of The Tempest

On a lonely desert island there lived a wise man called Prospero and his beautiful daughter Miranda. Prospero had once been the Duke of Milan, but his brother Antonio had wanted to become Duke himself. With the help of Alonso, the wicked King of Naples, Antonio had set Prospero and the 3-year-old Miranda adrift in a small boat. Prospero managed to take his magic books with him.

At last, Prospero and Miranda landed on an island. The wicked witch Sycorax had once lived there, but she had died just before Prospero arrived. The witch had trapped her servant Ariel in a tree. Prospero rescued him, and in return Ariel promised to be his servant forever. Prospero also found the ugly creature Caliban, the son of Sycorax, on the island. He put Ariel in charge of Caliban and set him to work. Many years passed on the island, and Prospero's powers as a magician grew as he studied his books.

One day he commanded Ariel to create an enormous storm. Miranda was worried for she saw a ship at sea, and thought that everyone on board would be killed.

"Don't worry, Miranda," Prospero said. "They will all be safe, and the ship will come safely in to port – but those on board will not be able to see it!"

It so happened that on the ship were Prospero's brother Antonio and the King of Naples, along with Sebastian, the King's brother, and Ferdinand, the King's son, and Gonzalo, an honest adviser. They were now in Prospero's power! Ferdinand was washed ashore first; he thought that Antonio and his father must be dead. Prospero sent Ariel to fetch him. Although Ariel was invisible, Ferdinand was able to follow his voice as he sang a song about Ferdinand's father:

Full fathom five thy father lies:
Of his bones are coral made:
Those are pearls that were his eyes:
Nothing of him that doth fade,
But doth suffer a sea-change
Into something rich and strange.
Sea-nymphs hourly ring his knell:
Hark! Now I hear them, ding-dong, bell.

Ferdinand was upset to hear this as he thought it meant that his father was dead. This wasn't true, however: Antonio and the King of Naples were lost on another part of the island.

When Ferdinand and Miranda met, they immediately fell in love. Prospero was secretly pleased at this, but he decided to test Ferdinand. He accused him of being a spy and set him to work carrying wood. Eventually, Ferdinand was able to prove to Prospero that he really did love Miranda.

Meanwhile, Ariel was having fun making Antonio, Alonso and Sebastian miserable. When he saw that they were hungry, he made a spell to create a table full of delicious food, but as soon as they started to eat he made it vanish. Then he appeared before them as a monster.

"You are being punished because of what you did to Prospero," he told them.

Antonio and the King said that they were truly sorry for what they had done. Ariel brought them to Prospero and they were amazed to see that he was alive. Antonio was very ashamed about what he had done to his brother, and the King of Naples pleaded with Prospero to forgive him too.

Prospero had one more surprise for them. He drew back a curtain and there were Ferdinand and Miranda together. It was agreed by everyone that Ferdinand would become the King of Naples and Miranda would be his queen.

Then they all returned to the ship, which they found safe in the harbour. Miraculously, no one had died in the terrible storm. Finally, Prospero gave Ariel his freedom. He buried his magic books, and never used magic again.

A Scene from The Tempest

In this scene, Ariel plays a trick on Antonio, Alonso, Gonzalo, Sebastian and Francisco, a lord, who are wandering, lost, on the island. Suddenly they hear strange music.

Alonso What harmony is this? My good friends, hark.

Gonzalo Marvellous sweet music.

(Enter spirits, in several strange shapes, bringing in a table and banquet, and dance about it. They invite the king and his friends to eat, then leave. Prospero, who is invisible, is watching them.)

Alonso What were these creatures?

Sebastian Now I will believe that there are unicorns!

Gonzalo If in Naples I should report this now, would they believe me, if I should say I saw such islanders? For certain these are people of the island who, though they are of monstrous shape, yet their manners are more gentle than any of human kind!

Prospero *(Aside)* Honest Lord, you have said well, for some of you there present are worse than devils.

Francisco They vanished strangely.

Sebastian No matter, since they have left their **viands** behind, for we have stomachs. Will it please you to taste of what is here?

Alonso Not I.

Gonzalo Faith, sir, you need not fear.

Alonso I will stand to and feed, although it may be the last time! Brother, my lord the Duke, stand to, and do as we.

*(They move the table. There is thunder and lightning. Ariel descends in the appearance of a **harpy** The banquet disappears.)*

Ariel You are three men of sin, unfit to live amongst men. Now destiny has cast you up on this island which men do not inhabit!

(Alonso, Sebastian and Antonio draw their swords.)

Ariel	You fools! My fellows and I are ministers of fate. You might as well try and wound the loud winds, or stab the sea to death, as harm a hair on my head! We are **invulnerable**. Now remember, you three from Milan overthrew Prospero, and exposed him and his innocent child to the sea. The sea and land, and all creatures, have come together to punish you. From now on your life on this **desolate** island will be everlasting torment!
	(Ariel disappears in thunder. Then, to soft music, the spirits enter again, and dance with mocks and bows. They go out, carrying out the table.)
Prospero	*(Aside to Ariel)* Bravely the figure of this harpy you have performed, my Ariel. My high charms have worked, and my enemies are now in my power.
Gonzalo	In the name of something holy, sir, why do you stand staring like that?
Alonso	O, it is monstrous, monstrous! I thought that the sea, the wind, even the thunder, spoke the name of Prospero and roared out my sin. My son is drowned, I'll seek him out and join him in death. *(Exit Alonso)*
Sebastian	Be there one **fiend** at a time, I'll fight all of them!
Antonio	I'll be your second.
	(Exit Sebastian and Antonio)
Gonzalo	*(To Francisco)* All three of them are desperate. Their great guilt begins to work on them like a poison. Follow them, and stop whatever this madness drives them to.

From *The Tempest*, Act 3, Scene 3

Glossary

viands	food
harpy	monster with wings and claws
invulnerable	cannot be harmed
desolate	uninhabited
fiend	devil

At the end of *The Tempest*, Prospero promises Ariel his freedom.
Ariel imagines his new life in this song:

Where the bee sucks, there suck I:
In a cowslip's bell I lie;
There I couch when owls do cry.
On the bat's back I do fly
After summer merrily.
Merrily, merrily, shall I live now
Under the blossom that hangs on the bough.
Merrily, merrily, shall I live now
Under the blossom that hangs on the bough.

From *The Tempest*, Act 5, Scene 1

Two Murders

Banquo's Ghost

Macbeth has murdered Duncan, King of Scotland, so that he can become King himself. He fears that his friend, Banquo, has guessed what he has done, so he arranges for Banquo and Banquo's son, Fleance, to be murdered.

In this scene from the play, Macbeth has invited Scottish noblemen to a feast.

Cast

Macbeth, King of Scotland

Lady Macbeth, his wife

Lennox, Ross, and other Lords of Scotland

A Murderer

Macbeth	At first and last a hearty welcome.
Lords	Thanks to your majesty.
Macbeth	Ourself will mingle with society and play the humble host.
Lady Macbeth	Pronounce it for me, sir, to all our friends, For my heart speaks they are welcome.
	(Enter Murderer)
Macbeth	Be large in mirth. Anon we'll drink a measure The table round. *(To Murderer)* There's blood upon thy face.
Murderer	*(Aside to Macbeth)* 'Tis Banquo's, then.
Macbeth	'Tis better thee without, than he within. Is he dispatched?

Murderer	My lord, his throat is cut. That I did for him.
Macbeth	Thou art the best of the cut throats. Yet he's good That did the like for Fleance.
Murderer	Most royal sir, Fleance is 'scaped.
Macbeth	Then comes my fit again! But Banquo's safe?
Murderer	Ay, my good lord. Safe in a ditch he bides, With twenty trenched gashes on his head.
Macbeth	Thanks for that. There the grown serpent lies. The worm that's fled Hath nature that in time will venom breed.

(Exit Murderer)

Lady Macbeth	My royal lord, You do not give the cheer.

(Enter the Ghost of Banquo, and sits in Macbeth's place.)

Macbeth	Now good digestion wait on appetite, And health on both.
Lennox	May it please your highness sit?
Macbeth	The table's full.
Lennox	Here is a place reserved, sir.
Macbeth	Where?
Lennox	Here, my good lord. What is't that moves your highness?
Macbeth	Which of you have done this?
Lords	What, my good lord?

Macbeth   *(To the Ghost)* Thou canst not say I did it. Never shake
Thy gory locks at me.

Ross   *(Rising)* Gentlemen, rise. His highness is not well.

Lady Macbeth *(Rising)* Sit, worthy friends. My lord is often thus,
And hath been from his youth.
The fit is momentary. Upon a thought
He will again be well. Feed, and regard him not.

(She speaks apart with Macbeth.)

Why do you make such faces? When all's done
You look but on a stool.

Macbeth	Prithee see there. Behold, look, how say you?
	Why, what care I? If thou canst nod, speak, too!

(Exit Ghost)

Lady Macbeth	What, quite unmanned in folly?
Macbeth	If I stand here, I saw him.
Lady Macbeth	Fie, for shame.
	(Aloud) My worthy lord,
	Your noble friends do lack you.
Macbeth	I do forget.
	Do not muse at me, my most worthy friends.
	I have a strange infirmity which is nothing
	To those that know me. Come, love and health to all,
	Then I'll sit down.
	(To an attendant) Give me some wine. Fill full.

(Enter Ghost)

	I drink to the general joy of the whole table,
	And to our dear friend Banquo, whom we miss.
	Would he were here. To all and him we thirst,
	And all to all.
Lords	Our duties, and the pledge.

(They drink)

Macbeth	*(Seeing the Ghost)* Avaunt, and quit my sight! Let
	the earth hide thee,
	Thy bones are marrowless, thy blood is cold.
Lady Macbeth	Think of this, good peers,
	But as a thing of custom.

Macbeth	Hence, horrible shadow, unreal mockery, hence!

(Exit Ghost)

Why so, being gone,
I am a man again. Pray you sit still.

Lady Macbeth	You have displaced the mirth, broke the good meeting
With most admired disorder.
Macbeth	Can such things be?
Can you behold such sights
And keep the natural ruby of your cheeks
When mine is blanched with fear?
Ross	What sights, my lord?
Lady Macbeth	Pray you, speak not. He grows worse and worse.
Question enrages him. At once, good night.
Stand not upon the order of your going,
But go at once.
Lennox	Good night, and better health
Attend his majesty.
Lady Macbeth	A kind good night to all.

(Exit Lords)

From *Macbeth*, Act 3, Scene 4

The Murder of Clarence

The wicked Richard Duke of Gloucester is determined to become King. To ensure this he arranges a series of murders, including that of his own brother, the Duke of Clarence.

In this scene from *Richard III*, Clarence is imprisoned in The Tower of London. One night he has a terrible dream of his own death. He imagines he is on a ship with his brother Gloucester …

Clarence   As we paced along
Upon the giddy footing of the hatches,
Methought that Gloucester stumbled; and, in falling,
Struck me, that thought to stay him, overboard,
Into the tumbling billows of the **main**
O Lord! methought what pain it was to drown:
What dreadful noise of water in mine ears,
What sights of ugly death within mine eyes!
Methought I saw a thousand fearful wrecks;
Ten thousand men that fishes gnawed upon;
Wedges of gold, great **ouches**, heaps of pearl,
Inestimable stones, unvalued jewels,
All scattered in the bottom of the sea.
Some lay in dead men's skulls; and in those holes
Where eyes did once inhabit, there were crept,
As 'twere in scorn of eyes, reflecting gems,
That wooed the slimy bottom of the deep,
And mocked the dead bones that lay scattered by.

From *Richard III*, Act 1, Scene 4

17

Later in the same scene, the murderers sent by Richard arrive at the Tower of London. The Duke of Clarence is asleep …

Second Murderer   What, shall I stab him as he sleeps?

First Murderer   No. He'll say 'twas done cowardly, when he wakes.

Second Murderer   Why, he shall never wake until the great judgement day.

First Murderer   Why, then he'll say we stabbed him sleeping.

Second Murderer   The urging of that word 'judgement' hath bred a kind of **remorse** in me.

First Murderer   What, art thou afraid?

Second Murderer Not to kill him, having a warrant, but to be damned for killing him, from the which no warrant can defend me.

First Murderer I thought thou hadst been **resolute**.

Second Murderer So I am – to let him live.

First Murderer I'll back to the Duke of Gloucester and tell him so.

Second Murderer Nay, I pray thee. Stay a little. I hope this **passionate humour** of mine will change. **It was wont to hold me but while one tells twenty**.

(He counts to twenty)

First Murderer	How dost thou feel thyself now?
Second Murderer	Some certain **dregs** of conscience are yet within me.
First Murderer	Remember our reward, when the deed's done.
Second Murderer	**'Swounds**, he dies. I had forgot the reward.
First Murderer	Where's thy conscience now?
Second Murderer	O, in the Duke of Gloucester's purse.
First Murderer	When he opens his purse to give us our reward, thy conscience flies out.
Second Murderer	'Tis no matter. Let it go. There's few or none will entertain it.
First Murderer	What if it come to thee again?
Second Murderer	I'll not meddle with it. It makes a man a coward. A man cannot steal but it accuseth him. A man cannot swear but it checks him. It fills a man full of obstacles. It made me once restore a purse of gold that by chance I found. Come, shall we fall to work?
First Murderer	Take him on the **costard** with the hilts of thy sword, and then throw him into the **malmsey butt** in the next room.
Second Murderer	O excellent **device** – and make a **sop** of him.
First Murderer	Soft, he wakes.
Second Murderer	Strike!
First Murderer	No, we'll reason with him.
Clarence	Where art thou, keeper? Give me a cup of wine.
Second Murderer	You shall have wine enough, my lord, anon.
Clarence	In God's name, what art thou?
First Murderer	A man, as you are.
Clarence	But not as I am, royal.

First Murderer	Nor you as we are, loyal.
Clarence	Thy voice is thunder, but thy looks are humble.
First Murderer	My voice is now the King's; my looks, mine own.
Clarence	How darkly and how deadly dost thou speak. Your eyes do menace me. Why look you pale? Who sent you **hither**? Wherefore do you come?
Second Murderer	To, to, to –
Clarence	To murder me.
Both Murderers	Ay, ay.

From *Richard III*, Act 1, Scene 4

Glossary

methought	I thought
main	sea
ouches	jewels
inestimable	uncountable
remorse	strong feeling of regret
resolute	determined
passionate humour	
	strong feeling or emotion
It was wont to hold me but while one tells twenty	
	It only held me back until I had counted up to twenty.
dregs	remains
'Swounds	God's wounds – a swear word
costard	head
malmsey butt	barrel of malmsey wine
device	idea
sop	bread soaked in wine
hither	here

A Midsummer Night's Dream

Puck Speaks to the Fairy

Puck, sometimes known as Robin Goodfellow, is a mischievous spirit who serves Oberon, the King of the Fairies. In this scene from the play, he meets a fairy, who is the servant of Titania, the Queen of the Fairies.

Oberon and Titania have had an argument. Titania stole a young Indian boy from an Indian Prince, and keeps him as a special servant. She is very fond of him. Oberon is jealous. He would like the boy as his own servant, but Titania will not give him up.

(Enter a Fairy at one door, and Puck at another.)

Puck   How now spirit, wither wander you?

Fairy   Over hill, over dale,
Thorough bush, thorough briar,
Over park, over **pale**,
Thorough flood, thorough fire –
I do wander everywhere
Swifter than the moon's sphere,
And I serve the fairy queen,
To **dew her orbs upon the green**.
The cowslips tall her **pensioners** be;
In their gold coats, spots you see –
Those be rubies, fairy **favours**;
In those freckles live their savours.
I must go seek some dewdrops here,
And hang a pearl in every cowslip's ear.
Farewell, thou **lob** of spirits; I'll be gone.
Our Queen and all her elves come here anon.

Puck
The King doth keep his **revels** here tonight.
Take heed the Queen come not within his sight,
For Oberon is **passing fell and wrath**
Because that she as her attendant hath
A lovely boy stolen from an Indian king.
She never had so sweet a **changeling**,
And jealous Oberon would have the child
Knight of his train, to trace the forests wild.
But she **perforce** withholds the loved boy,
Crowns him with flowers, and makes him all her joy.
And now they never meet – in grove or green,
By fountain clear or spangled **starlight sheen** –
But they do **square**, that all their elves for fear
Creep into acorn cups and hide them there.

Fairy
Either I mistake your shape and making quite,
Or else you are that **shrewd and knavish sprite**
Called Robin Goodfellow. Are not you he
That frights the maidens of the villagery,
Skim milk, and sometimes **labour in the quern**,
Bootless make the breathless housewife churn,
And sometime make the drink to bear no **barm**,
Mislead night-wanderers, laughing at their harm?
Those that "Hobgoblin" call you, and "Sweet Puck",
You do their work, and they shall have good luck.
Are not you he?

Puck   Thou speakest aright:
I am that merry wanderer of the night.
I jest to Oberon, and make him smile
When I a fat and bean-fed horse beguile,
Neighing in likeness of a filly foal;
And sometime lurk I in a **gossip's** bowl
In very likeness of a **roasted crab**;
And when she drinks, against her lips I bob,
And on her withered dewlap pour the ale.
The wisest aunt telling the saddest tale
Sometime for three-foot stool mistaketh me;
Then slip I from her bum. Down topples she,
And "Tailor" cries, and falls into a cough;
And then the whole **choir** hold their hips and laugh,
And **waxen in their mirth**, and sneeze, and swear
A merrier hour was never wasted there.
But make room, Fairy: here comes Oberon.

Fairy   And here my mistress. Would that he were gone!

From *A Midsummer Night's Dream,* Act 2, Scene 1

Glossary

pale	fence
dew her orbs upon the green	
	cover the fairy rings with dew
pensioners	finely dressed servants that served Queen Elizabeth I
favours	gifts
lob	clown
revels	celebrations
passing fell and wrath	
	in a furious temper
changeling	a stolen child
perforce	by force
starlight sheen	the shining of stars
square	quarrel, argue
shrewd and knavish sprite	
	clever and mischievous spirit
skim milk	take the cream from the top of the milk
labour in the quern	work (or play tricks) in the grindstone, when people are grinding corn
bootless make the breathless housewife churn	
	make the housewife's churning useless, that is, stop the milk turning into butter
barm	the froth on top of beer – Puck makes the beer taste flat
mislead	lead in the wrong direction
when I a fat and bean-fed horse beguile	
	when I play tricks on old, fat horses
gossip	person who likes to talk about other people
roasted crab	roasted crab apple
and on her withered dewlap pour the ale	
	Puck makes the ale pour down the drinker's chin
and "Tailor" cries	people traditionally cried "Tailor" when they fell over – it is not known why
choir	the assembled people
waxen in their mirth	laugh louder and louder

Pyramus and Thisbe

At the end of *A Midsummer Night's Dream* a group of villagers present a performance of a play, 'Pyramus and Thisbe', at the wedding of Theseus, Duke of Athens, to Hippolyta. They try very hard, but they are not very good actors!

In the play Pyramus and Thisbe are in love, but their parents refuse to let them see each other. As their houses are next door to each other, they are able to speak through a crack in the wall. They arrange a secret meeting at the tomb of Ninus. When Thisbe arrives at the tomb, she is frightened off by a lion, who tears the coat she has dropped with his blood-soaked jaws. When Pyramus arrives, he thinks that Thisbe has been killed by the lion, and so he kills himself. When Thisbe returns, she finds Pyramus dead; in her grief, she stabs herself to death.

The Performers

Bottom the weaver – Pyramus
Flute the bellows mender – Thisbe
Snout the tinker – the wall
Snug the joiner – the lion
Starveling the tailor – moonshine
Quince the carpenter – Prologue (introduces the play)

The Audience

The Audience
Theseus
Hippolyta
Demetrius

(Enter the cast of the play)

Quince (Prologue)　This man is Pyramus, if you would know;
This beauteous lady Thisbe is, certain.
This man with **lime and roughcast** doth present
Wall – that vile wall which did these lovers **sunder**.
This man with lantern, dog and bush of thorn
Presenteth moonshine. This grisly beast –
Which lion hight by name – the trusty Thisbe did
affright.

Snout (the wall)　In this same **interlude** it doth befall
That I – one Snout by name – present a wall.
And such a wall as I would have you think
That had in it a crannied hole or chink,
Through which the lovers, Pyramus and Thisbe,
Did whisper often very secretly.

Bottom (Pyramus)　O grim-looked night, O night with hue so black,
O night which ever art when day is not!
O night, O night, alack, alack, alack,
I fear my Thisbe's promise is forgot.
And thou, O wall, O sweet and lovely wall,
That standest between her father's ground and mine,
Thou wall, O wall, O sweet and lovely wall,
Show me thy chink to blink through with mine **eyne**.

(Enter Flute as Thisbe)

Flute (Thisbe)　O wall, full often hast though heard my moans
For parting my fair Pyramus and me.

Bottom　I see a voice. Now will I to the chink
To spy if I can hear my Thisbe's face. Thisbe!

Flute　My love! Thou art my love, I think?

Bottom　Will thou at Ninny's tomb meet me straight away?

Flute	Tide life, tide death, I come without delay.
Snout	Thus have I, wall, my part **discharged** so: And being done, thus wall away doth go.
Hippolyta	This is the silliest stuff that ever I heard.
Theseus	The best in this kind are but shadows; and the worst are no worse, if imagination amend them. Here come two noble beasts; a man and lion.

Snug (as the lion)   You ladies – you whose gentle hearts do fear
The smallest monstrous mouse that creeps on floor –
May now, **perchance**, both quake and tremble here
When lion rough in wildest rage doth roar.

**Starveling
(as moonshine)**   This lantern doth the horned moon present;
Myself the man in the moon doth seem to be.

(Enter Flute)

Flute   This is old Ninny's tomb. Where is my love?

*(Enter Snug, who roars. Thisbe runs off. The lion
tears Thisbe's **mantle**, then exits.)*

Theseus   Well run, Thisbe!

Demetrius   Well roared, lion!

(Enter Bottom)

Bottom   What dreadful **dole** is here?
Eyes, do you see?
How can it be?
O dainty duck, O dear!
Thy mantle good
What, stained with blood?
Come tears, confound,
Out sword, and wound
The **pap** of Pyramus.
Thus die I – thus, thus, thus.

(Enter Flute)

Flute	Asleep, my love?
	What, dead, my dove?
	O Pyramus, arise.
	Speak, speak. Quite dumb?
	Dead, dead? A tomb
	Must cover thy sweet eyes.
	Come trusty sword,
	Come blade, my breast imbrue

(She stabs herself)

And farewell friends
Thus Thisbe ends.
Adieu!

From *A Midsummer Night's Dream*, Act 5, Scene 1

Glossary

lime and roughcast	materials to make a wall
sunder	split apart
interlude	short play
eyne	eye
discharged	completed
perchance	perhaps
mantle	coat
dole	dismal event
pap	breast
imbrue	stab, make bleed

Time-line: 1550–1620

Shakespeare's Life	Year	Key Events

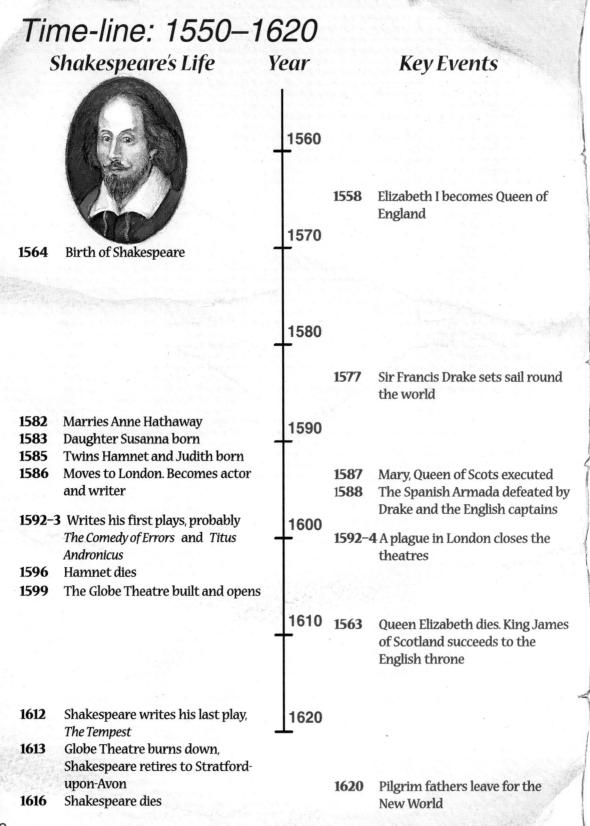

1560

1558 Elizabeth I becomes Queen of England

1570

1564 Birth of Shakespeare

1580

1577 Sir Francis Drake sets sail round the world

1582 Marries Anne Hathaway
1583 Daughter Susanna born
1585 Twins Hamnet and Judith born
1586 Moves to London. Becomes actor and writer

1590

1587 Mary, Queen of Scots executed
1588 The Spanish Armada defeated by Drake and the English captains

1592–3 Writes his first plays, probably *The Comedy of Errors* and *Titus Andronicus*
1596 Hamnet dies
1599 The Globe Theatre built and opens

1600

1592–4 A plague in London closes the theatres

1610

1563 Queen Elizabeth dies. King James of Scotland succeeds to the English throne

1612 Shakespeare writes his last play, *The Tempest*
1613 Globe Theatre burns down, Shakespeare retires to Stratford-upon-Avon
1616 Shakespeare dies

1620

1620 Pilgrim fathers leave for the New World